CONTENTS

ONE LAZY SUMMER'S DAY...

BE QUIET NOW TUFFY, OR TOM WILL WAKE UP!

WHILST HE DREAMS OF SHEEP WE TAKE AWAY HIS GOAT'S CHEESE...

I THINK THIS WILL BE ENOUGH!

WAIT UP... PHEEW.. THIS IS HEAVY...

THAT'S BETTER... I MUST BE STRONGER THAN I THINK! THIS PEAR DOESN'T WEIGH MUCH!

I CAN'T REMEMBER INVITING YOU TO LUNCH... SO MAYBE I'LL HAVE YOU *FOR* LUNCH INSTEAD!

I BET PEAR AND MOUSE GO WELL TOGETHER!

HELP! HE WAS GONNA EAT ME! YOU SAVED MY LIFE!

IT'S COWARDLY TO ATTACK SOMEONE FROM BEHIND!

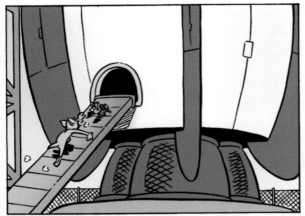

Continued on page 14

spot the difference

Can you spot 10 differences between these two pictures?

Answers: different music note in whistle smoke, logo added to train, Tom has a hat, colour of Jerry's scarf, chain is missing from train, teapot replacing headlamp, doughnut on Tom's mouth, colour change to star on the front of train, use trap on Tom's tail, Tuffy rides the train.

MARBLE

FOLLOW THESE EASY STEPS TO MAKE YOUR OWN
MARVELLOUS MARBLE MAZE!

You will need:
A shoe box lid
18 Lolly sticks
A pen or pencil
Thin card
A marble
Paint and glue

1 Paint your shoe box lid with your favourite colours, and leave it to dry.

2 When it's dry choose a start and finish point – they need to be on diagonally opposite corners of your shoe box!

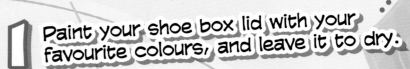

3 To make your maze, glue all but two of the lolly sticks into the lid on their thin sides. Make sure that you leave enough space for the marble to easily roll between the sticks!

MAYHEM!

4

Draw and paint pictures of Tom and Jerry onto thin card, cut them out, and stick them onto lolly sticks. Glue Tom at the start of your maze, and Jerry at the finish!

5

Poke a hole in the lid, with the tip of a pen or pencil, next to Jerry, for your marble to roll out off, when you have completed the maze!

NOW YOU'RE READY TO PLAY!

USE YOUR MARBLE MASTERY TO MANOEUVRE THE MARBLE THROUGH THE BARRIERS, AND OUT OF THE HOLE AT THE OTHER END!

13

Continued from page 9

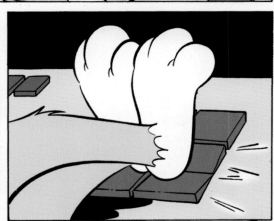

Continued on page 21

SEEING DOTS

Join the dots to see what Tom and Jerry are up to. When you have finished colour the scene in!

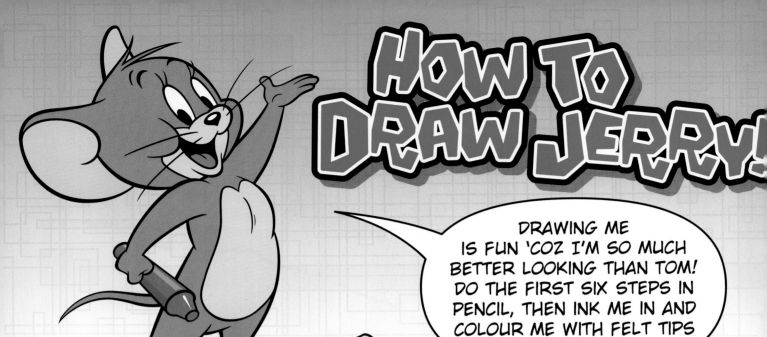

HOW TO DRAW JERRY!

DRAWING ME IS FUN 'COZ I'M SO MUCH BETTER LOOKING THAN TOM! DO THE FIRST SIX STEPS IN PENCIL, THEN INK ME IN AND COLOUR ME WITH FELT TIPS OR CRAYONS.

1

START WITH 'A LINE OF ACTION', THIS HELPS US TO GET JERRY'S POSE RIGHT. ADD A CIRCLE FOR THE HEAD AND A BEAN SHAPE FOR THE BODY.

2

ADD THE BASIC SHAPES FOR THE ARMS, LEGS, HANDS AND FEET.

3

IMPROVE THE SHAPE OF JERRY'S HEAD. ADD THE EARS AND TAIL.

4

NOW START TO GET IN SOME OF THE DETAIL. MAKE SURE TO GET THE EYES AND NOSE IN THE RIGHT PLACE. NOTICE THAT THE NOSE IS ALL IN THE LOWER PART OF THE HEAD CIRCLE.

5

ADD MORE DETAILS - THIS IS EASY AS LONG AS YOU'VE GOT THE NOSE AND EYES RIGHT.

6

NOW PUT IN THE REST OF THE DETAIL. DON'T FORGET THE WHISKERS AND THE PATCH TO JERRY'S BODY. FINALLY INK OVER THE DRAWING IN PEN. DON'T INK IN THE LINES THAT WERE ONLY THERE AS CONSTRUCTION. CAREFULLY RUB OUT THE PENCIL AND YOU'RE DONE.

Continued from page 18

21

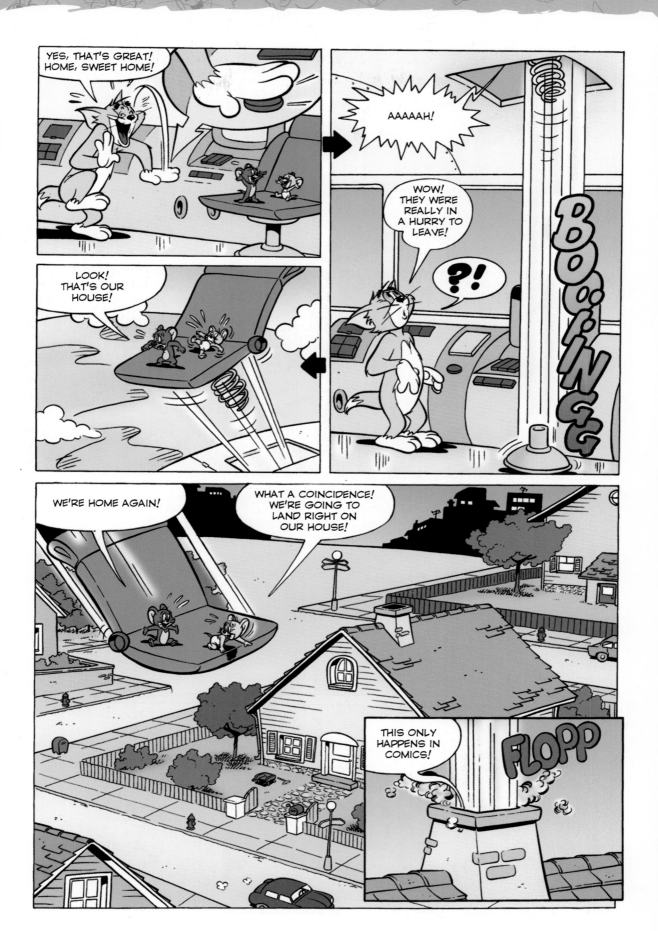

23

FARMYARD FUN

Tom & Jerry have been to the farm. Can you spot all their favourite farmyard animals hidden in the grid?

Tick as you find:

Cow ☐

Sheep ☐

Chicken ☐

Duck ☐

Horse ☐

Goat ☐

Pig ☐

Cat ☐

S	S	J	S	S	S	H	L	U	F	I
Q	J	S	G	I	Z	O	O	B	S
I	I	P	H	I	I	E	C	D	X
Y	S	A	C	E	P	D	H	U	I
B	M	N	T	M	E	G	I	C	N
H	X	O	U	B	R	P	C	K	O
O	T	O	G	T	L	O	K	L	P
R	A	K	A	O	W	W	E	Q	Y
S	O	C	F	R	F	F	N	T	V
E	G	H	M	V	P	K	P	Y	Q

ANSWERS:

26

Silly Shadows

Can you match each Tom & Jerry pose up wth their shadows?

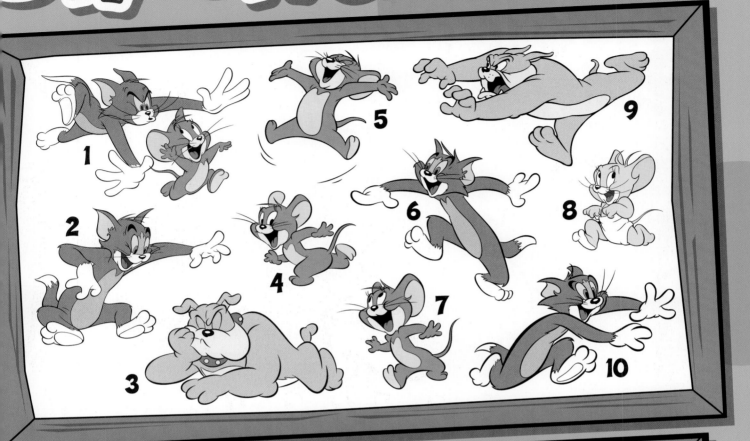

a =   b =   c =   d =   e =

f =   j =   h =   i =   j =

27

Eye Spy!

Another normal day of cat and mouse with Tom & Jerry! Can you spot the hidden items?

THAT EVENING...

HE'LL SOON BE REALLY IN THE DARK!

GOOD! I LIKE CANDLE-LIGHT!

EVERYTHING'S GOING AS PLANNED. EVEN THE MISCHIEVOUS MICE ARE AWAY!

JUST AS I PLANNED! ALL THE LIGHTS WENT OUT!

WHAT HAPPENED?

MY CROWN HAS BEEN *STOLEN!*

I'LL SOON HAVE THE MONEY FOR MY MOUSE-PROOF HOUSE!

STOP! THIEF!

NO MORE HEROIC ACTS!

HA HA! WE DIDN'T TELL M'SIEUR CAT THERE WAS A PLANK MISSING!

SO IT WAS THE CAT!

AND SO...

LET ME OUT!

NOW YOU'VE GOT EXACTLY WHAT YOU WANTED!

OH YES -- THAT HOUSE IS DEFINITELY MOUSE-PROOF!

END

KITCHEN CHAOS!

The fridge has just been filled with yummy food. Play this game with a friend and see who can get back to the kitchen first!

How to play

You will need two counters and a dice. Each player takes it in turn to throw the dice and whoever scores highest goes first. Take it in turns to move around the spaces, avoiding all the obstacles if you can!

The first player to make it to the Kitchen is the winner!

Ask an adult to help you cut out these counters or make your own if you don't want to spoil your annual.

7

8

6 Put on your skates and move to space 10

5

4

24

3 You fall in a hole. Miss a turn.

23

2

1

START

TOM and JERRY™ in A Day at the Beach

THIS IS WHAT HAPPENED WHEN TOM, JERRY AND TUFFY SPENT THE DAY TOGETHER AT THE BEACH. AS YOU MIGHT'VE GUESSED, THEY DIDN'T GET ALONG...

Continued on page 42

SUMMER COLOURS

Grab your pens and add some colour to this summer scene!

Continued from page 40

Continued on page 48

45

Tasty Treats!

Make these tasty tongue tickling recipes to give your taste buds a special treat!

Strawberry Smoothie Lolli

You'll need:

- 2 cups of chopped strawberries.
- 2 cups of vanilla yoghurt.
- 12 small paper cups.
- 12 lolly sticks.
- Cling film or foil.

1. Mix the strawberries and yoghurt in a bowl.

2. Fill the cups with the mixture and cover with cling film or foil. Then push a lolly stick through each one.

3. Freeze overnight, peel the paper cups off, then get munching!

Fruity Popsicles!

You'll need:

- 3 cups of mixed fruit juice.
- 400g can of sweetened condensed milk.
- cup of lemon juice.
- 12 small paper cups.
- 12 lolly sticks.
- A whisk.

ASK AN ADULT FOR HELP

1. Whisk the condensed milk and juices together.

2. Pour the mixture into the paper cups and put in the freezer.

3. Take out after one hour and place lolly sticks in the centre of each one.

4. Freeze for at least 5 hours, peel off the paper cups and they're ready to eat!

1. Mix all the ingredients together into a large jug.

2. Pour into glasses filled with ice cubes.

Traditional Lemonade!

You'll need:

- 2 cups water.
- 1/2 cup sugar.
- 1/4 cup lemon juice.
- Ice cubes.

47

Continued from page 45

FWISSHH

51

MEANWHILE ..
WOW! WHAT A SUDDEN CHANGE IN THE WEATHER
UH-OH! I'VE GOT TROUBLE!
GULP!
SPLASCH

THE END

SEASIDE PUZZLER!

Tom and Jerry are relaxing at the beach. Can you solve this seaside picture puzzler and fit all the seaside objects in the grid below?

DOWN

ACROSS

ANSWERS:

53

Continued on page 59

57

Missing Pieces!

Which three jigsaw pieces are needed to complete the picture below?

58

Continued from page 57

THE END